D1650084

Published by
Kandour Ltd
1-3 Colebrooke Place
London N1 8HZ
United Kingdom

This edition published in 2005 for
Bookmart Ltd
Registered Number 2372865
Trading As Bookmart Ltd
Blaby Road
Wigston
Leicester LE18 4SE



Design: G.M.Georgiou
Author: Colin Dempsey
Managing Editor: Kaspa Hazlewood



Printed and bound in India

ISBN: 1-904756-41-7

# MY ANCIENT ROMAN COLOURING BOOK

# INTRODUCTION

Beginning in the third century BC, the city of Rome built an empire that stretched from Spain in the west to Syria in the east and from Britain in the north to Egypt in the south. The Roman Empire did not fall until the fifth century AD. Its importance in world history has been immense. It was through the Romans that the art, literature and ideas of ancient Greece survived and through the Romans that the Christian religion spread through Europe. European languages like Italian, French and Spanish come directly from Latin, the language of the Romans; those that do not, such as English and German, contain large numbers of Latin words. The influence of Roman architecture can be seen in cities all over the world. Law and systems of government owe a huge debt to ancient Rome. The fascination with Rome continues today in novels, poetry, films and in the museums, art galleries and historical sites visited by millions of people every year.

Richard Woff

Head of Schools and Young Audiences Education at the British Museum

At the British Museum you can see many wonderful objects from Rome and its empire and you can visit the Museum online at www.thebritishmuseum.ac.uk/childrenscompass

ROME
CORSICA
SARDINIA
Mediterranean Sea
SICILY

# ROMAN FAMILY

That little boy will probably grow up to follow his father's footsteps into the Senate. None of the hard life of a soldier or a slave for him. He will eat the best food and drink the best wine.

Notice how many times his father's toga is folded, and the complicated braiding of his mother's hair. She would never be able to do that without the help of her servants.

# CAVALRY AND MERCENARY

See how this horseman's shield differs to the round shield of the high officer. This is because a long shield will protect more of his body when he is seated on his horse. Can you see why? Here's a clue. Think about his legs.

A mercenary is a man who sells his services to an army of a country other than his own. This mercenary is from one of the many Germanic tribes conquered by Rome. He is a soldier on foot with a long sword and a javelin for throwing at the enemy.

# GLADIATORS

Think you could take on these two nasty individuals or even one of them? Think again. These are gladiators who train every day in the art of combat. Whereas you might go to school to learn reading and writing and counting, these men learned only one thing : how to kill.

The man on the left is a retarius. His speciality was trapping you in his net and then spearing you with his trident.

The other gladiator would try to stab you with his evil-looking sword. Who do you think would win if they fought each other?

# HAIRSTYLES AND HATS

Here are some ancient Roman hats and hairstyles. Do you see any that are still in fashion today?

# CENTURION

A Centurion usually began his career in the Roman army as a legionary. As a Centurion he was in charge of a hundred men. To show who he was, he wore his gladius (the soldier's sword) and his dagger on different sides to the legionary.

His armour was silver-plated. Underneath the armour he would wear a tunic. He had sandals on his feet and leg guards to protect his shins. On his head he wore a helmet with a large crest.

# DOORKNOBS

Here are two Roman doorknockers. The one on the right looks like a satyr with a goat's horns and the one on the left might be Medusa with serpent tails for hair. Placed on the front door they would stop evil spirits entering the house.

# TABLE LEGS

Here are a couple of table legs. They are an example of the beautiful ancient Roman craftsmanship. On the right the carving is of the magic wand of the Greek god Hermes, who was known as Mercury by the Romans. It has two serpents entwined and a pair of wings. That is Mercury at the top in his winged helmet. On the left are clusters of grapes which made the wine that the Romans were so fond of.

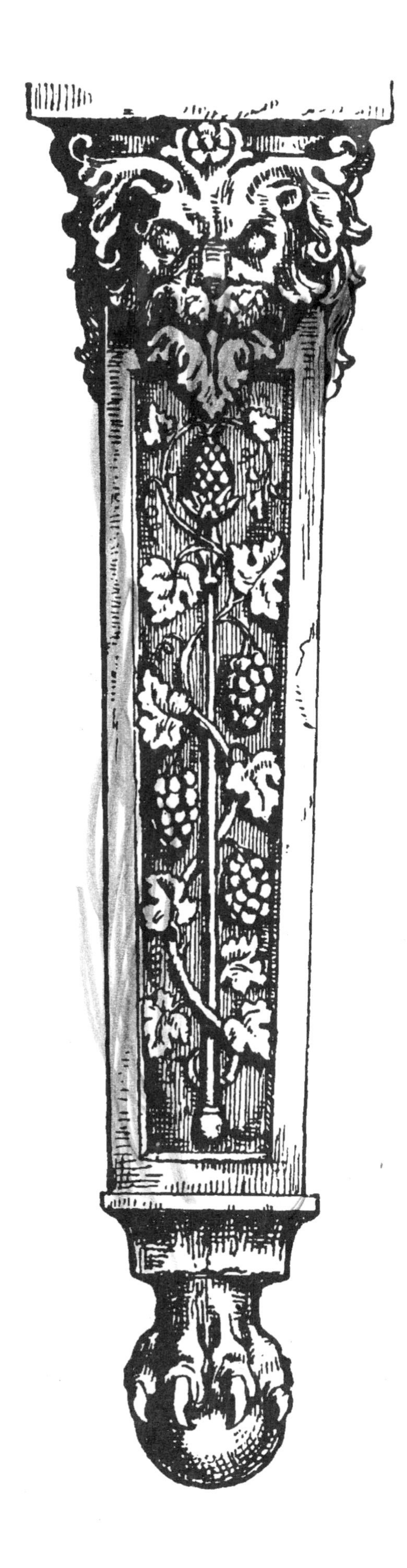

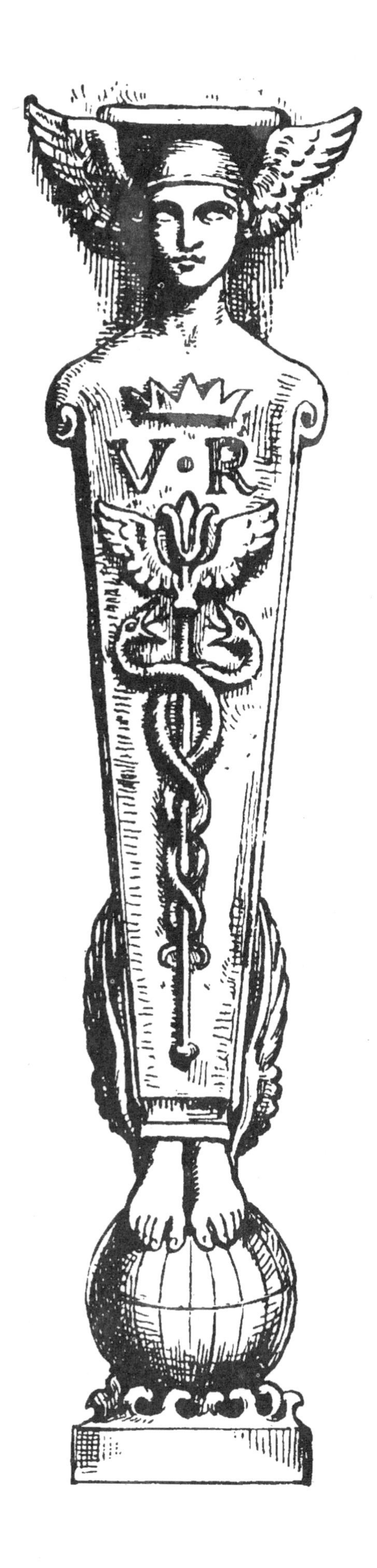
V·R

# FOUNTAINS

Rome received all of its water through a system of aqueducts. All water flowed to the city by gravity, from the surrounding hills and was stored in large cisterns very similar to today's water towers.

Water flowed from the cisterns either through pipes to individual houses or to public distribution points. Fountains served both decorative and functional purposes, since people could bring their buckets to the fountain to collect water. The cisterns provided the height needed to generate water pressure for the fountains to spray.

# CORNUCOPIA

This is a carving of the cornucopia or the Horn of Plenty. It is stuffed to overflowing with good things to eat.

The story goes that when the Greek God Zeus was playing with the goat Amalthea, he accidentally broke off one of her horns. To make up for this, Zeus promised Amalthea that the horn would always be full of whatever fruits she desired.

This became the cornucopia of the Roman goddess Copia.

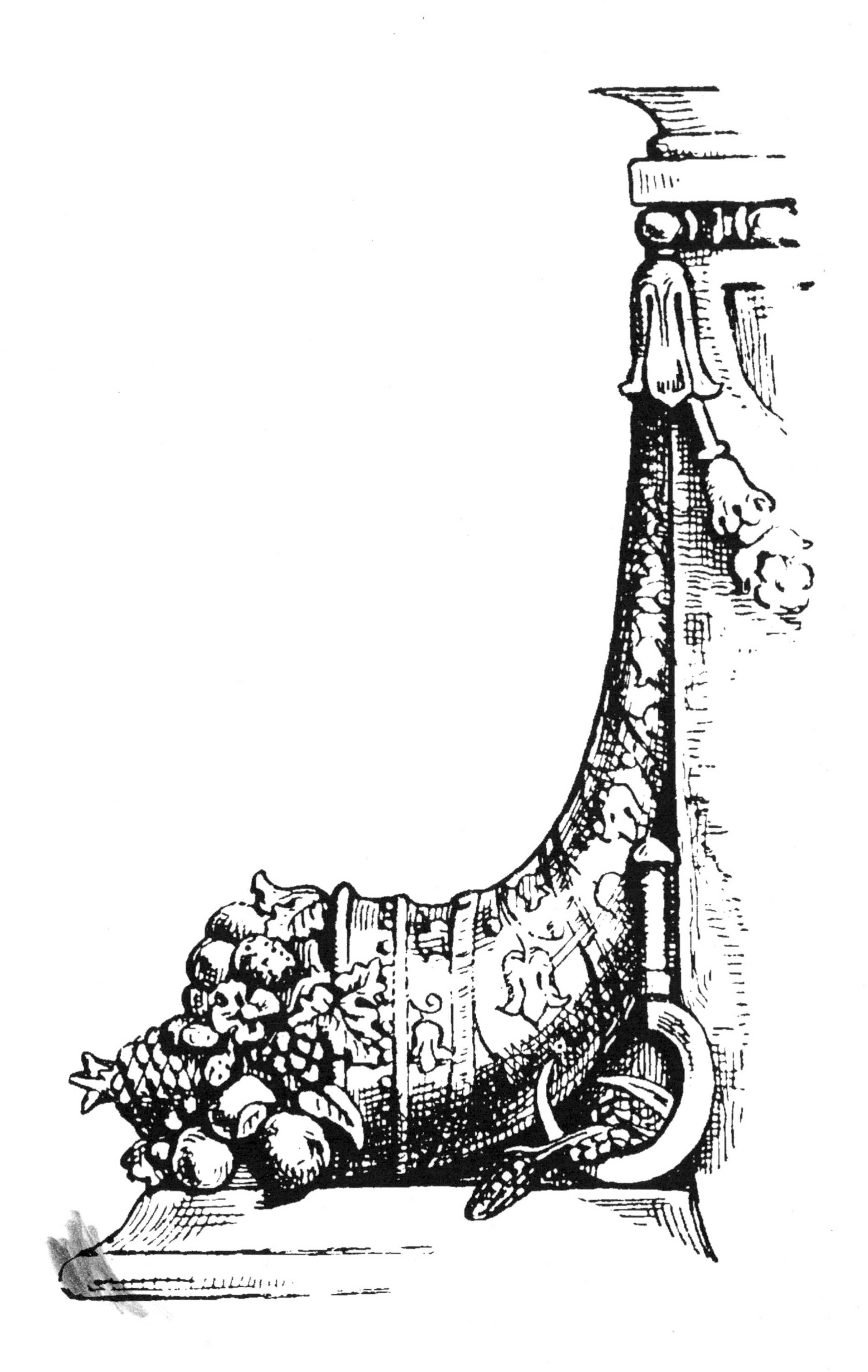

# ELEPHANTS

The Romans were defeated in a battle against Hannibal by the sudden appearance of their enemies seated on the backs of elephants. They must have made a terrifying spectacle. Imagine the noise, the sound and the crushing hooves of an elephant rushing towards you, especially if you have never seen one before.

The Romans soon became very fond of elephants and the writer Pliny tells us that the Romans thought that elephants could understand Latin and worshipped the sun and moon!

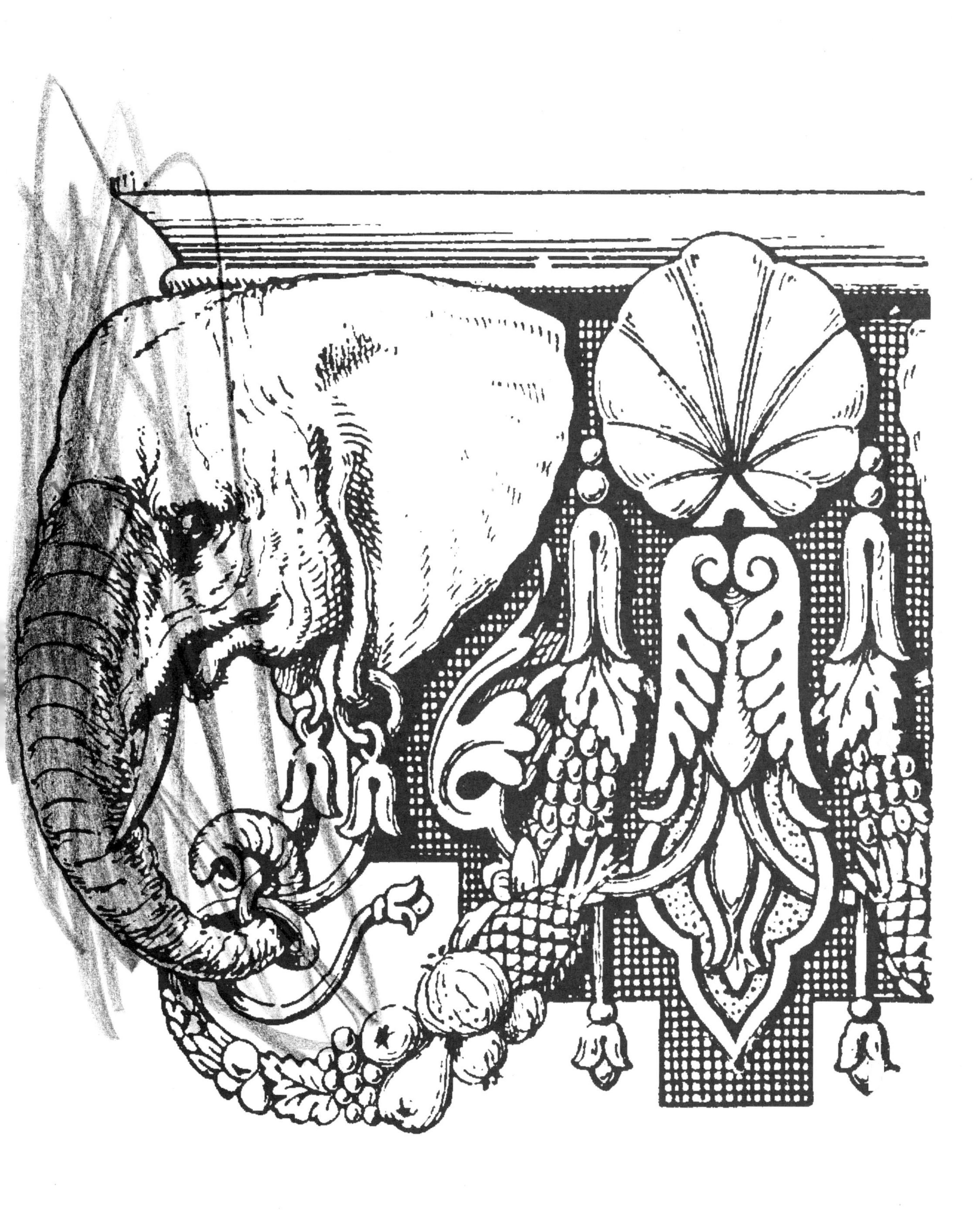

# FURNITURE

Houses changed greatly while Rome was growing. At first they were small and simple, with little decoration. Bright colours were used simply and appealingly to brighten interiors. As the empire grew and the Romans became wealthier, they became much more ornate. Roman furniture was usually made from rare and expensive materials such as marble and ivory.

They would sometimes decorate their furniture with mythological creatures such as Medusa.

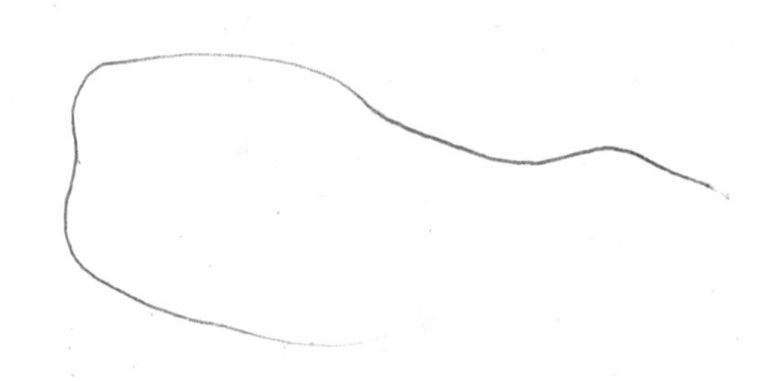

# BOARS

The Romans were very fond of boars. Just like Obelix in the adventures of Asterix. No feast was complete unless the table was groaning under the weight of a roast boar or two. But they were very difficult to catch because when they were cornered they could suddenly turn round and attack with their sharp tusks.

# SINE METU

Sine Metu is Latin for "Without Fear". It comes from a quote by Seneca, who said "Optanda mors est, sine metu mortis mori" which means "To die without fear of death is to be desired."

Seneca was a Roman philosopher who had been the tutor of Nero, the infamous Roman emperor. When he fell from favour he was ordered to kill himself. This he did with great dignity, without fear of death.

SINE METU
I
L

# SPQR

The Roman army was divided up into legions and each legion consisted of about 5,000 men. The legions carried banners into war with pictures of eagles and the letters SPQR which stood for the Latin phrase Senatus Populusque Romanus, meaning 'The Senate and the People of Rome'.

Sometimes the banners also had pictures of the twins Romulus and Remus, who were left to drown at the edge of the flooding Tiber River by their uncle. A she-wolf found them and took pity on them and gave them milk to drink. As men, the brothers returned to the spot where they had been abandoned and founded the city of Rome.

It survives to this day as the coat of arms of modern Rome. You can see the letters on manhole covers and the exteriors of civic buildings.

A more humourous meaning of the meaning of SPQR is the Italian phrase "Sono pazzi questi Romani", which translates into "These Romans are crazy". The comic book character Obelix often uses it.

SPQR

# ARMOUR

This helmet has a neck guard at the back and cheek guards in case the soldier was hit from the side. The crest at the top might have offered some protection from a crushing blow to the head.

He had a dagger for fighting close up and a short sword for stabbing called a gladius. The Barbarians preferred a longer sword for slashing.

He also wore a "Lorica Segmentata" over his chest which consisted of steel plates hinged together, rivetted to leather straps. This made him very flexible and safe on the battlefield.

# POTTERY

Roman pottery was rarely painted, as it had been in Greece. Most of it was made locally until the time of Augustus, when large factories sprang up which could make pottery quickly and cheaply and then transport it along the new roads that connected the Empire.

The Romans had learned new techniques from the parts of Western Asia that they had conquered which enabled them to decorate the pottery by pushing the clay into plaster moulds. The quality was good and these factories made a great deal of money.

# MONEY

Coins that had a guaranteed value were invented around 650BC. They were stamped with a promise by a government that they were worth a certain amount, so that whoever received it could work out how much bread he could buy with it, for example.

The Romans figured out that if they ran out of gold to make the coins they used to pay their soldiers, they could mix the gold with silver and if they ran out of silver they could mix in bronze.

A Roman emperor would have new coins stamped with a picture of his face in profile, which means from the side. So when we find some archaeological treasure we can tell how old it is by checking the face of the emperor on the coin.

# THE COLOSSEUM

The Colosseum was a huge Roman arena built in the shape of an oval. It could seat up to 50,000 spectators who came to watch gladiators fighting to the death, ferocious battles between wild beasts, and early Christians thrown to the lions for sport. The Romans certainly had blood-thirsty tastes!

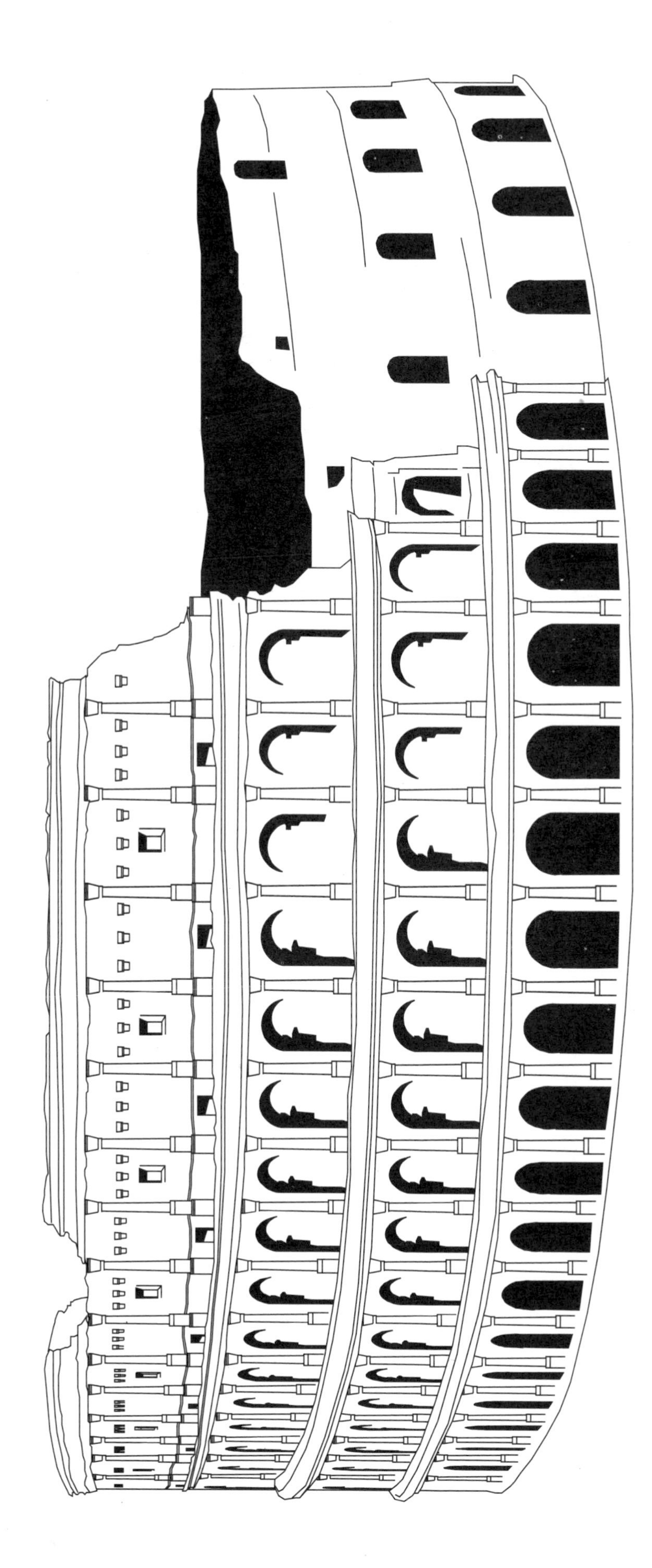

# THE COLOSSEUM

The Colosseum or Flavian Amphitheatre was begun by Vespasian, inaugurated by Titus in 80 AD and completed by Domitian. It was the first permanent amphitheatre to be built in Rome. Its monumental size and grandeur as well as its practical and efficient organisation for producing spectacles and controlling the large crowds make it one of the great architectural monuments achieved by the ancient Romans.

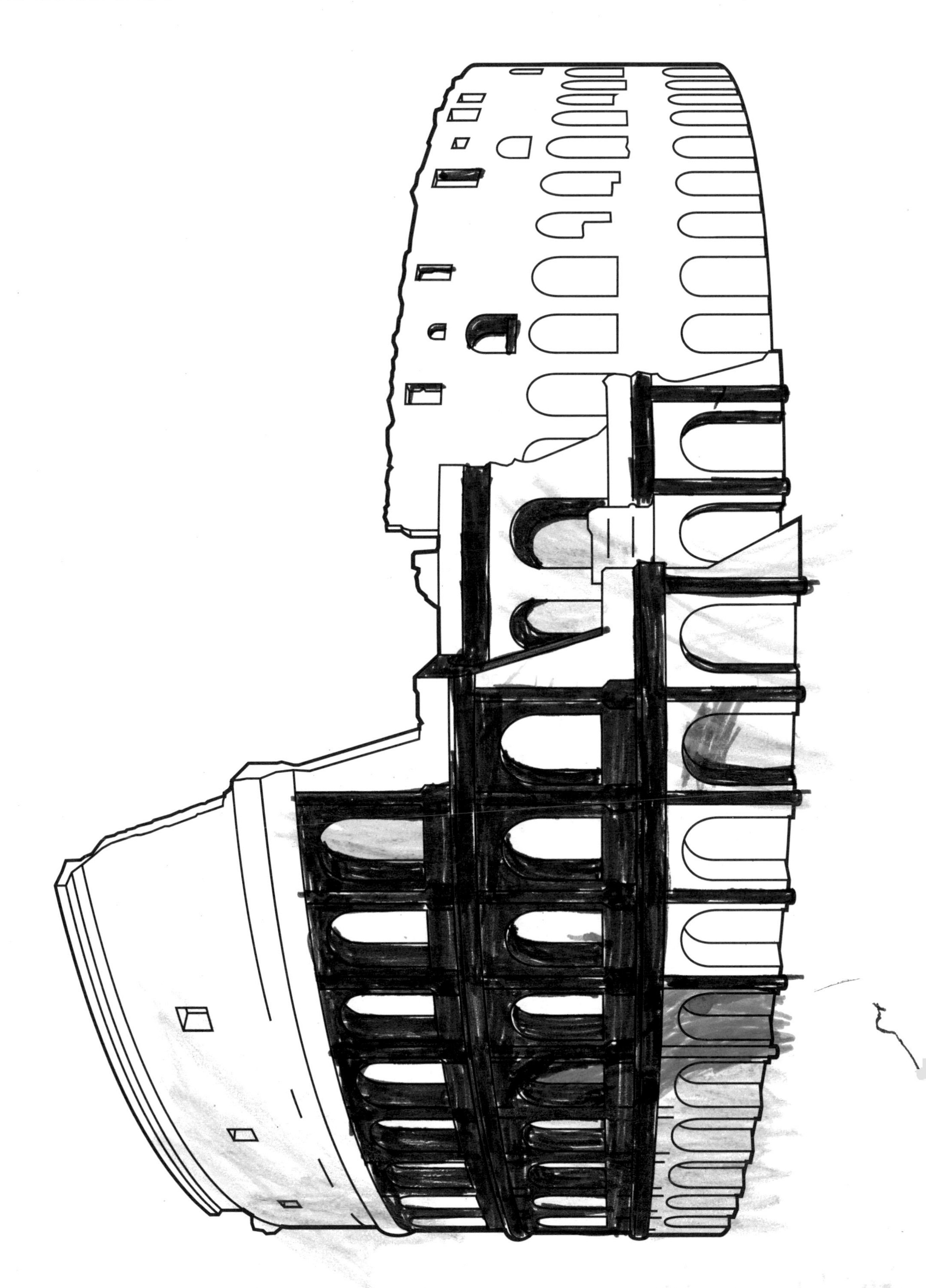

# PANTHEON

The word "pantheon" means a temple dedicated to all the gods, rather than to just one god. This is the Pantheon at Rome, built in the second century by the Emperor Hadrian, after the first Pantheon was destroyed in the great fire of 80 AD, and then the second Pantheon was hit by lightening.

Third time lucky eh?

Hadrian was obsessed with ancient Greece and he wanted to build something that would look like a classical Greek temple and his Pantheon was considered so beautiful that Michelangelo, the famous sculptor, thought it was built not by men, but by angels.

It was changed into a Catholic Church, after the Romans had stopped worshipping their old gods and became Christians.

As the sun moves in the sky, sunlight enters through a hole in the top of the dome and it makes beautiful patterns across the marble floor.

# THE SATYR

The ancient people were fond of combining different animals together and even animals and men or women. Just think of the Sphinx and even nowadays we have the Hippogriff. Can you think of any others? Satyrs come from Greek mythology. They looked very strange, covered in hair, with horns and goats' legs and they drank too much wine so they were always singing and dancing!

# GRIFFIN

This strange creature with the wings of an eagle on top of a lion's body is called a griffin. They probably came from the ancient Middle East because we see lots of them in Persian sculpture. It was a protective symbol, ever watchful.

# SENATOR

The Senate decided how to rule the Roman Republic just like the British Government today for example runs Great Britain. Because the Roman Empire grew so large it became difficult to control so Caesar increased the number of senators in the senate to 900 but we all know what happened to him don't we? After his death the number went down to 600, perhaps because they had become too powerful.

By the sixth century its influence was so small that it disappeared altogether.

# PLINY THE ELDER

When Mt. Vesuvius erupted in 79AD the Roman fleet under the command of Pliny the Elder was stationed across the Bay of Naples at Misenum. Pliny launched ships and sailed toward the erupting volcano for a closer look and to attempt a rescue. Rescue was not possible and Pliny died during the eruption, not in the streets of Pompeii, but across the bay at Stabiae.

# CENTURION

This is a Roman foot soldier. He would throw his javelin at the enemy, hoping to kill him or leave it sticking out of his shield, making it difficult to carry. Then he would rush forward and stab with his gladius, the short sword. Sometimes if the enemy was firing arrows he would make a tight formation with his fellow soldiers, hiding behind their shields.

# AUGUSTUS

Emperor Augustus was the heir of Julius Caesar but his world was turned upside down when Caesar was murdered.

Marc Antony married his sister, but deserted her for Cleopatra, Queen of Egypt. Augustus was so outraged by this that he declared war on him and soon defeated him.

By the time he died, the Empire stretched from the forests of Gaul (modern-day France) to the deserts of Egypt. This was possible because he was such a great road builder. Remember the straight Roman roads?

After his death, the people of Rome worshipped Augustus as a god.

# BRUTUS

Think you can trust your friends? Well how well do you really know them? Brutus was supposedly a good friend of Julius Caesar, he was even related to him. You might think this was a good reason to tell Caesar of any plans to kill him but no, Brutus, actually joined in the plans, in what we call a "conspiracy".

On March 15, on a day now known as the "Ides of March", Brutus walked with Caesar to the Forum in Rome and when he gave the signal to the other "conspirators" they surrounded Caesar and murdered him.

Some friend eh?

Caesar was so upset by the way he was betrayed by Brutus that his last words were "Et tu Brutus?", which is Latin for "You too Brutus?"

The people of Rome and the Roman army would not forgive the men who had killed their leader and they had to hide themselves but eventually fate caught up with Brutus and he himself was killed.

# JULIUS CAESAR

Julius Caesar wasn't an Emperor but he started it all by becoming dictator of Rome. In 45BC Caesar was given absolute power over Rome. But within a year he was dead. In 44BC he was assassinated and his "heir" Augustus became the first real Emperor of Rome.

This was a man whose mistress and mother of his child was one of the most famous women in history, Cleopatra Queen of Egypt.

But here he was stabbed to death by men who were supposed to be his friends and followers. And he was carried out of the Forum where he lay in a pool of his blood by three common slaves.

How the mighty fall.

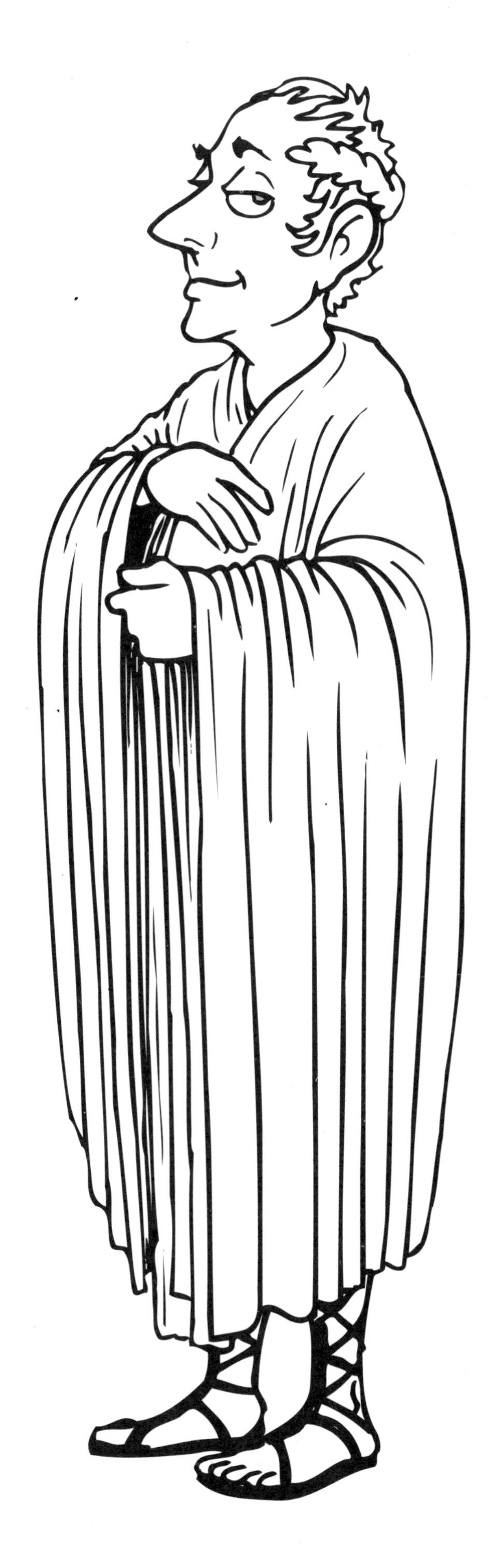

# NERO

Nero was one of the most infamous Roman Emperors ever. By the time he was 25 he had already murdered his wife, his mother and his step brother, Britannicus! When a great fire broke out which destroyed half of Rome he blamed the Christians and then he turned his murderous intentions on them! There were several attempts to get rid of him and these were brutally put down by him. Yet more murders!

In the end, even his own bodyguards could stand him no longer and in a cowardly act he took his own life to avoid being brought to justice. After he died, the Romans tried to forget he ever existed, so ashamed were they by his bad behaviour.

When Rome burned, legend has it that mad Nero played the violin while he watched the city in flames from his palace.

# THE CATAPULT

Before tanks, fighter planes and before even cannons were invented, the Romans used catapults to fire missiles at their enemies. Sometimes they fired large rocks or jars of burning oil to break up any defenses that the enemy were using to hide behind. Sometimes they fired huge arrows at the soldiers themselves, breaking up the lines of soldiers called "ranks".

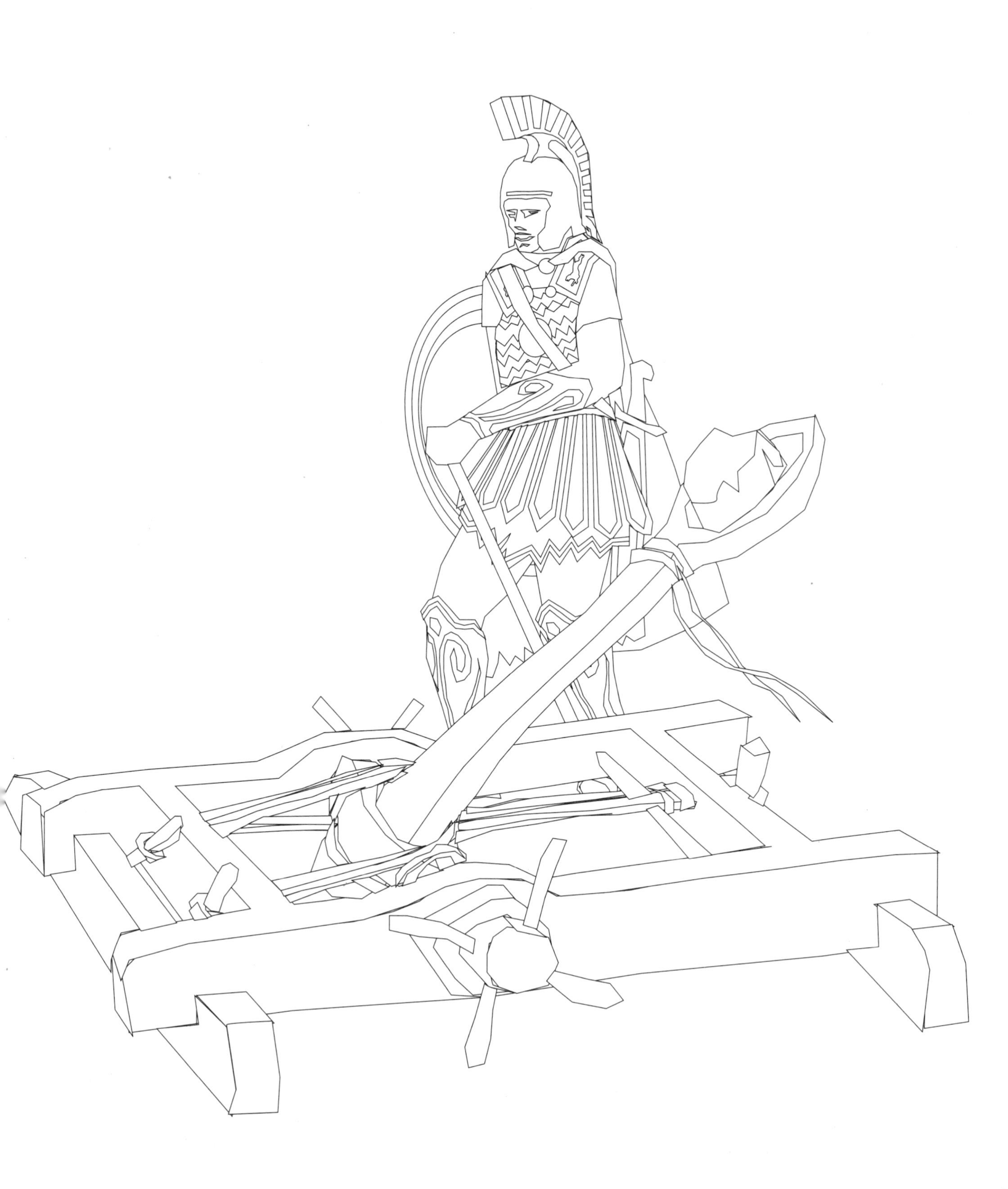

# CATAPULT

The Catapult gave the Romans a great advantage over their enemies as they could hold a siege at a fortification and place the catapults for maximum efficiency.

The Greeks invented the catapult and the Romans had Greeks work mechanics working for them.

The main structure was wooden with ropes of horsehair and sinew.

# GRAPES AND WINE

Grapes grew all over the Mediterranean in ancient times but the Romans were more interested in establishing their Empire.

By the middle of the second century BC, they had control of the Mediterranean and their thoughts turned to business.

Huge vineyards worked by slaves came to dominate the countryside and many of the poor farmers who had only ever grown enough to feed their own family had to move to the city.

Wine was exported all over the Empire, especially to Gaul, where they loved the stuff.

A cheap wine made sweet with honey was often given out at public spectacles, such as gladiator fights, and cattle were even given the dregs from the bottom of the wine press. Slaves had to make do with the grape stalks and skins, left in water to ferment.

# WINE AND BREAD

This is a jar or amphora for storing liquid. It could contain water, wine or olive oil. The Romans sometimes mixed wine with their water.

Sometimes the base of the jar was not flat but pointed and the Romans would stick it into the ground.

# OLIVES

Have you ever tasted olive oil? Chances are your parents are very fond of it. No one is sure who was the first to grow olives but one myth tells how Athena and Poseidon had a competition to see who would be the god of Athens. Poseidon struck the ground of the Acropolis and out gushed a stream of salty water which no one could drink. Athena however produced something much more useful, an olive tree which gave forth delicious juicy olives.

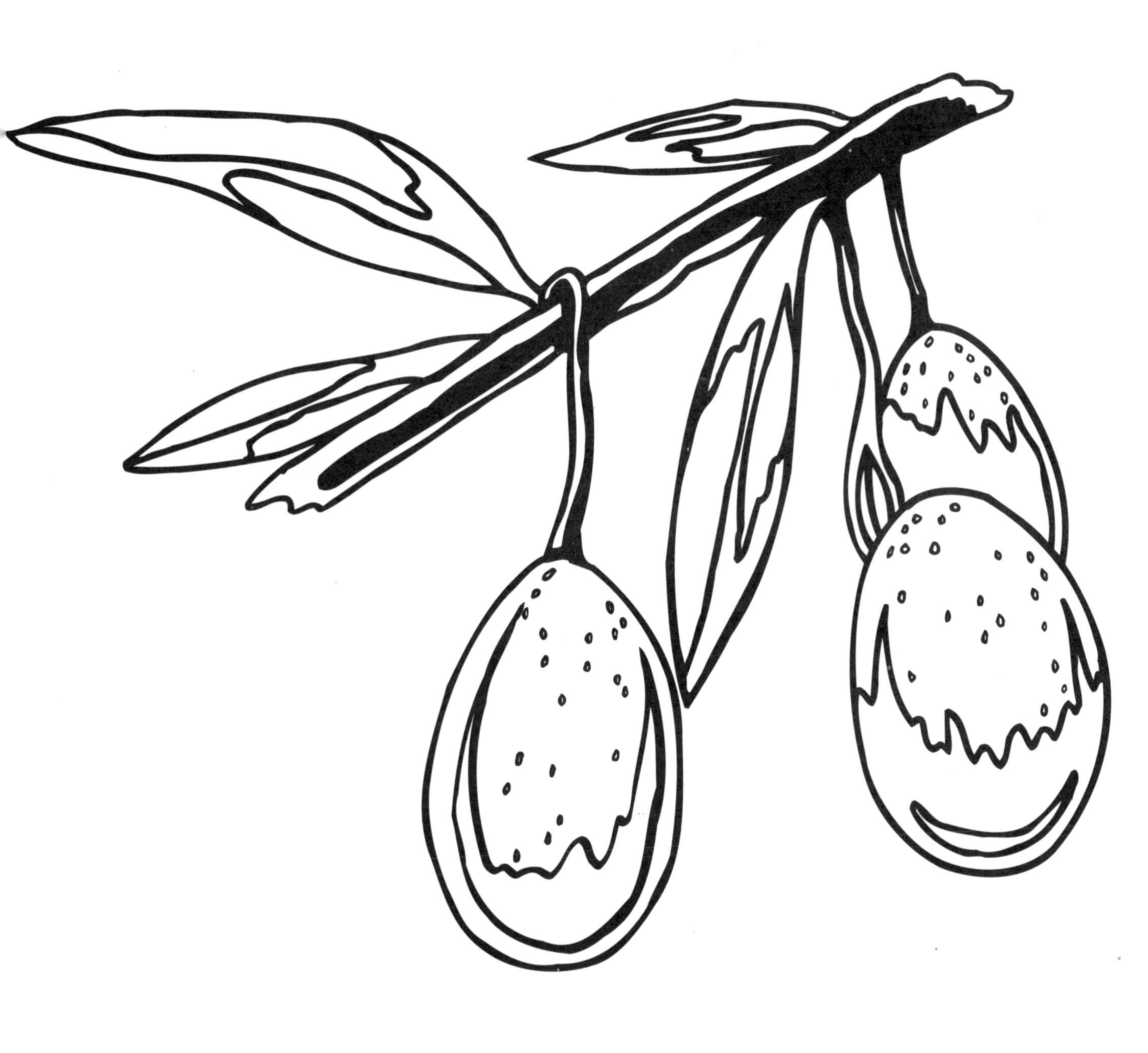

# COLUMNS

Here are a pair of Corinthian columns. The Romans found them very pretty and often used them in their buildings. When you next go into town see if you can spot any examples of the classical style.

# COLUMNS

Here are a pair of Corinthian columns. They are the most slender of the three classic Greek columns. The other two styles are Doric and Ionic. If you become an architect when you grow up you will study the classical styles of building.

# COLUMNS

Although they might look like table legs these are actually more examples of columns. The Romans and Greeks had to use many more columns than we do nowadays because they did not have the technology to hold up the roof of a large building without columns to support it.

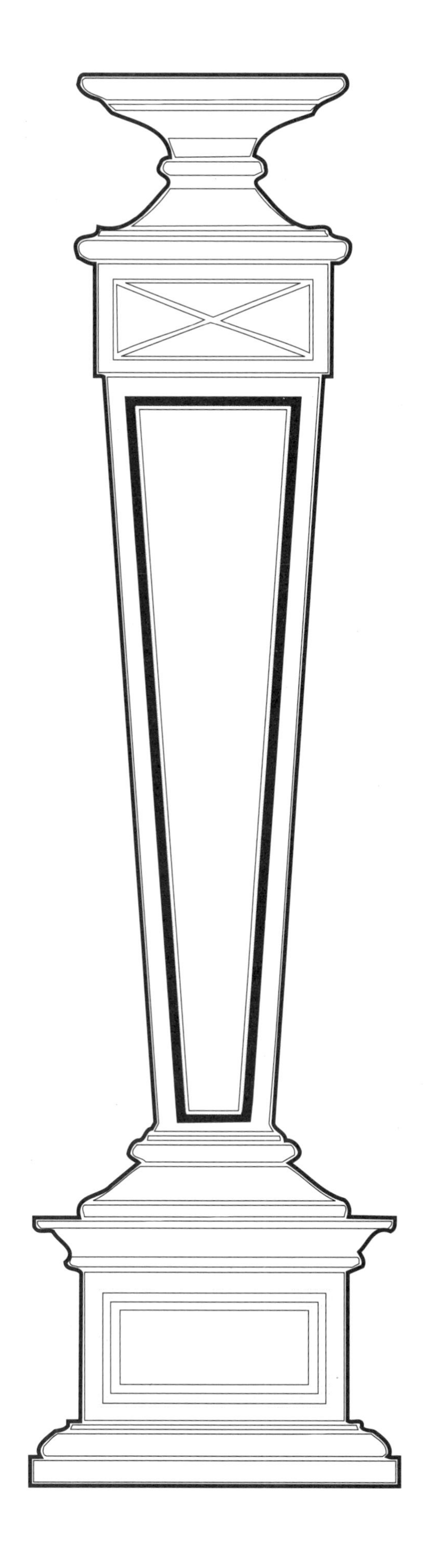

# NUMERALS 1–6

The Romans were great traders, buying and selling goods from the far-flung corners of the Empire. It is impossible to trade goods without a counting system, and this is why Roman numerals developed.

Unlike the Arabic system which we use today, the Roman numerals did not include a zero.

You can still see Roman numerals if you watch a film and wait until the end of the credits. There you will see a collection of letters which show when the film was made.

They are also used if there is more than one king or queen with the same name. How many can you think of?

I = 1

II = 2

III = 3

IV means to subtract I from V, leaving 4

V = 5

VI = 6

# NUMERALS 7–30

VII = 7

VIII = 8

IX means to subtract I from X, leaving 9

X = 10

XX = 20

XXX = 30

VII
VIII
IX
X
XX
XXX

# NUMERALS 40-400

XL means to subtract X from L, leaving 40

L = 50

C = 100

CC = 200

CCC = 300

CD means to subtract C from D, leaving 400

# NUMERALS 500–1000

D = 500

DC = 600

DCC = 700

DCCC = 800

CM means to subtract C from M, leaving 900

M = 1,000

D
DC
DCC
DCCC
CM
M

# PATRICIANS

The Romans were divided into two different classes. The Patricians and the Plebeians. This is a Roman Patrician, the ruling class of Rome. He was probably a well-paid official. To show his high status, he wears his distinctive tunic and sandals decorated with an ivory crescent.

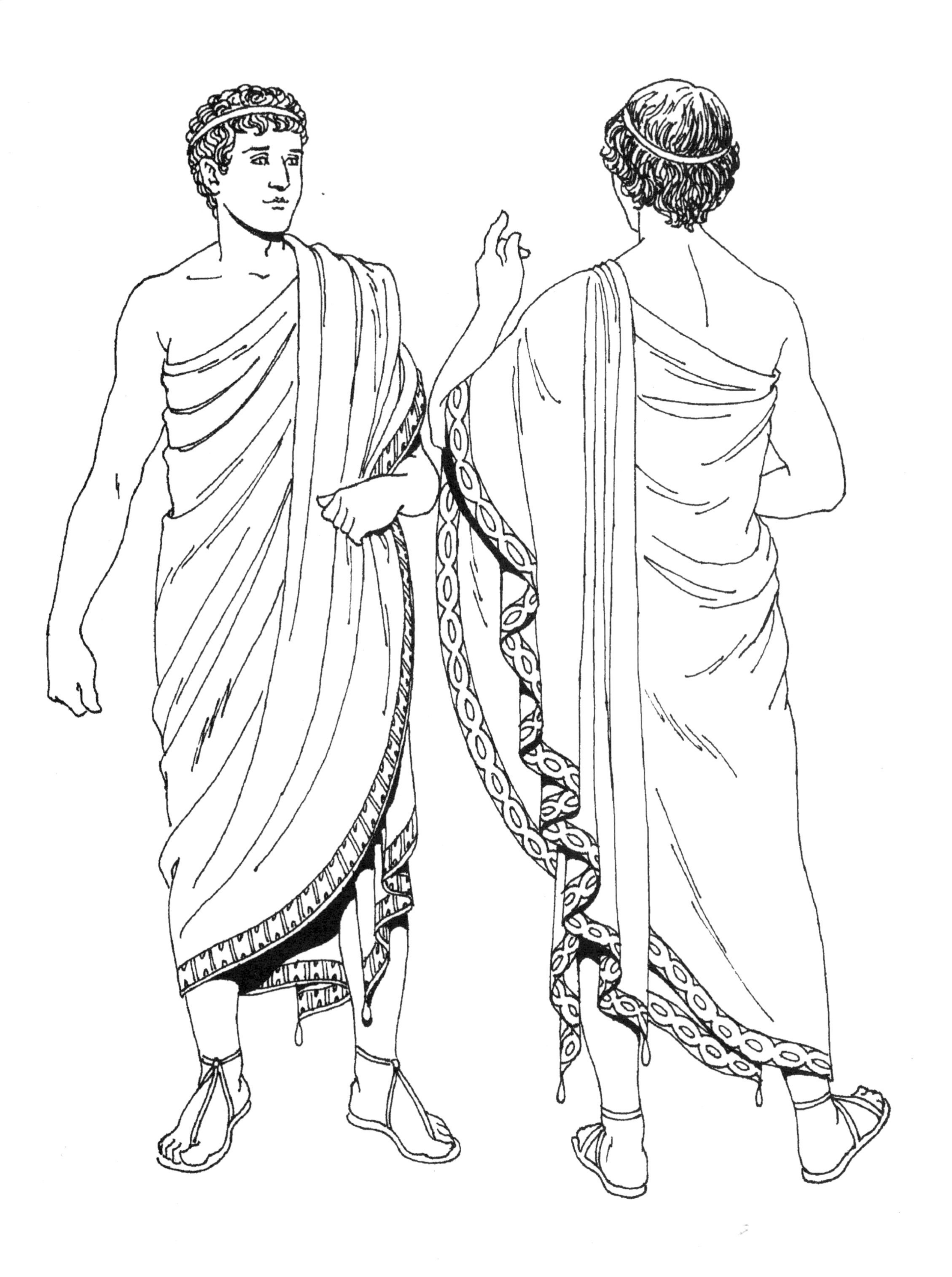

# SENATOR AND HIS WIFE

This is a Roman senator and his wife. A senator was a very powerful and rich man, like a politician nowadays. At first sight you might think he is dressed identically to his wife. But there are some differences. How many can you spot?

# PLEBEIANS

This man and wife are members of the plebeian class, ordinary everyday people like you or me. He would have to work hard for his living though not as hard as a slave. Maybe he had a small farm or a vineyard to make wine which was the favourite drink of the Romans.

# ROMAN OFFICER

This high officer in the Roman army is not as important as a Centurion. He only has leather armour. His shield is round like the classic shield of the ancient Greeks.

# NOTES